A Sinterklaas Story

Curious Clara's Amsterdam ADVENTURES

Order this book or find out more about the upcoming adventures of Curious Clara
at www.CuriousClara.com

ISBN: 978-90-814007-2-5

Text copyright © Maike Mehlert & Ken Carroll 2009
Illustration copyright © Rachelle Meyer 2009 www.rachellemeyer.com
Moral rights asserted

Printed in Belgium by Proost.

Curious Clara's Amsterdam Adventures
A Sinterklaas Story

Written by Maike Mehlert & Ken Carroll

Illustrated by Rachelle Meyer

To the Dutch tradition of Sinterklaas and to all the joy it brings to children everywhere.

In The Netherlands the Dutch tradition of *Sinterklaas* is a celebration of the feast of Saint Nicholas. It begins in early November when Sinterklaas arrives by boat from Spain along with his many helpers and his horse Amarigo, and ends on Saint Nicholas Evening (December 5) which is the main present-giving occasion for children. In Dutch this is called *pakjesavond* ("presents evening").

Throughout November Sinterklaas visits children in schools and other public places. Children are encouraged to learn poems and songs to sing to Sinterklaas. During the visits his helpers (called *Zwarte Pieten*) throw candy and *pepernoten* (small pieces of cake like candy) around.

Sinterklaas carries with him a book which contains the names of all children and states whether they have been good or naughty throughout the year.

On *pakjesavond* the tradition is that Sinterklaas and his helpers will climb down the chimney and will leave presents in the children's shoes which are placed by the fireplace, but that naughty children are taken away in a bag back to Spain.

It's December 4th and Clara is excited because it's only one more day before *pakjesavond*, the evening Sinterklaas delivers presents in The Netherlands.

As Clara arrives at school her teacher has a big surprise for them. "Today Sinterklaas is going to visit us and he will want to hear all the poems and songs you have been rehearsing."

Just then they hear a "Hello, children!" and
Sinterklaas enters. "*Goedemorgen*, Sinterklaas,"
reply the children as he sits down on a big chair
in front of the class.

The children take their turns reading and singing. Finally, it's Clara's turn. As she is reading her poem to Sinterklaas she notices little Bobby putting away a big shiny book, but she is busy with her poem and thinks nothing more of it.

When they have finished, each child receives a small gift. "Thank you very much for such a wonderful time," says Sinterklaas, and, together with his helpers and Amerigo, he waves goodbye and heads off to visit the rest of the children in the city.

That evening Sinterklaas is about to read the names of the children he will be visiting tomorrow. "Oh no, my book, it's gone!" shouts Sinterklaas. "Without the book, I won't know whom to deliver the presents to on *pakjesavond*!"

The next morning, while Clara is having breakfast with her mama, they hear the news on the radio "...and if Sinterklaas' book is not found, *pakjesavond* will have to be cancelled this year."

Suddenly Clara remembers Bobby. "I think I may know where Sinterklaas' book is!"

Clara cycles to Bobby's house and finds him looking very unhappy. "Hello Bobby, are you okay?" asks Clara.

Bobby tells Clara about the book. "I did many naughty things this year, that's why I took the book."

"But Bobby, you haven't been that naughty," says Clara and reminds him of some of the good things he has done.

"Shall we return the book to Sinterklaas?" asks Clara. "But how will we find him?" wonders Bobby.

Clara has an idea. ''The animals! They will know where to find Sinterklaas." Clara explains a well-kept secret: throughout the year the animals in Amsterdam keep a watch on the children and tell Sinterklaas who has been good or naughty.

Outside by the canal, Clara and Bobby summon as many of the animals as they can. "Can you help us deliver a message to Sinterklaas?" asks Clara, "Bobby has his book!" The animals all nod and head off to find Sinterklaas.

Clara and Bobby don't have to wait long before they hear the hooves of a horse echoing along the canal, and then, as if by magic, Sinterklaas appears on Amarigo.

Clara explains why Bobby took the book. "I see in my book that sometimes you are very naughty and sometimes good!" says Sinterklaas, and he thanks them for returning the book. "Now I have to go, as I have many children to visit, but I **will** be seeing you both again tonight."

Later that evening, Clara, just like children everywhere in The Netherlands, waits and hopes for a visit from Sinterklaas.

Suddenly there is a knock on the door. "It's Sinterklaas!" shouts Papa, and Clara looks out the window just in time to see Armarigo galloping off into the night. Papa goes outside and returns with Clara's clogs, an armful of presents and a very special golden envelope.

Dear Clara,

   Thank you for saving pakjesavond this year. If you hadn't been so curious, we may never have found my book, and the good children may never have gotten any presents. As a special thank you I'd like to invite you and your family to come visit me in Spain, and for you to learn to ride Amarigo.

   Your friend,

   Sinterklaas

So, wherever you are, and whatever you do, be good to the animals – because you never know what they may tell Sinterklaas.